Tales of Ancien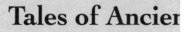

Enid Blyton

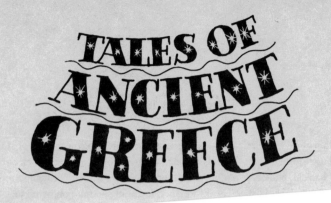

TALES OF ANCIENT GREECE

Enid Blyton

Illustrated by Chris Price

SCHOLASTIC INC.

New York   Toronto   London   Auckland   Sydney
Mexico City   New Delhi   Hong Kong

Enid Blyton

ISBN 0-439-17599-2

Copyright © 1930 Enid Blyton Limited.
Cover illustration © 1998 by Rosemary Woods.
Inside illustrations © 1998 by Chris Price. All rights reserved. Published by Scholastic Inc., 555 Broadway, New York, NY 10012, by arrangement with Element Books Inc. SCHOLASTIC and associated logos are trademarks and/or registered trademarks of Scholastic Inc.

Enid Blyton's signature is a trademark of Enid Blyton Limited.

12 11 10 9 8 7 6 5 4 3 2 1   0 1 2 3 4 5/0

Printed in the U.S.A.   X 5739   40

First Scholastic printing, February 2000

The moral right of the author and illustrator have been asserted.

Cover design by Gabrielle Morton

Contents

Pandora and the Whispering Box

Long ago, when the world was new, and no pain or sorrow was known, Epimetheus lived with his beautiful young wife Pandora. They dwelt in a house made of branches and leaves, for the sun shone always, and the wind was never cold.

Everyone was happy. Merry voices came on the breeze, and laughter was heard everywhere. Epimetheus and Pandora were happiest of all, for they loved one another very dearly, and were never apart.

One day, as they were dancing beneath the trees, they saw the god Mercury coming towards them. He carried a wooden box on his shoulder, and looked tired and hot.

"Ask him what he has in that box," said Pandora to Epimetheus. But Mercury would not tell them.

"That is not for you to know," he answered. "Will you permit me to put my box in your dwelling and leave it there for a while? I have far to go, and the weight of it makes my steps slow. I will call for it on my way back."

"We will take care of it for you," said Epimetheus. "Put it in a corner of our house. It will be safe there."

"Do not open it," said Mercury warningly. "You will never cease to regret it, if you do."

"We shall not even look at it," said Epimetheus. "You

need not fear, Mercury."

So the god placed his box on the ground in a corner of Pandora's dwelling. Then, bidding the two farewell, he set off again through the forest.

Pandora was filled with curiosity to know what was in the box. She left Epimetheus to dance with his companions, and stole into the house alone. She looked at the box for a long time, and then her eyes opened wide in astonishment.

The box was whispering! Little sighs and tiny sounds came from it. Pandora felt more curious than ever. There must be something alive inside to make that whispering noise.

She ran to the box and knelt down by it. It was very beautiful, made of finely-wrought dark wood, and on the top was a prettily carved head that seemed to smile at Pandora. Round the box was a strong, golden cord, tied in a tight knot.

The whispering went on and on. Pandora listened, but she could not hear what was said. Her fingers trembled to undo the cord – but just then Epimetheus came in to beg her to come and play with him.

"Oh, Epimetheus, I wish I knew what was in this box," said Pandora longingly. "Do you think I might just peep?"

Epimetheus was shocked.

"Mercury said that we were not to know," he said. "Come away, Pandora. Come and play with me in the sunshine, where everyone is happy."

But Pandora would not go. Epimetheus looked at her in surprise, and then, thinking that she would surely come if he left her alone, he ran out to his comrades.

Pandora heard the laughter and shouts of her friends, but she thought of nothing but the whispering box. Would it matter if she just undid the golden cord? Surely she could do that without harm.

She looked round to see if Epimetheus was really gone, then she turned eagerly to the box. He clever fingers worked at the golden cord, but it was so tight that she could not loosen it for a long time.

"Pandora, Pandora, come and dance!" cried her companions outside. But the maiden would not answer. She must undo the cord; she could not be happy until she had.

She pulled it and shook it. The knot was tight and difficult to untie. Pandora almost gave it up. Then suddenly it loosened, and swiftly she undid it. The golden cord slid on to the floor – and there lay the box, ready to open at a touch.

"Now that I have undone the cord, it is stupid not to open the box," thought the maiden. "Shall I just lift up the lid, peep inside, and then let it drop? What harm could that do to any one? I really must find out what makes the whispering noise."

She put her ear to the lid, and listened. Then, quite clearly, she heard tiny voices.

"Pandora, sweet Pandora!" they said. "Let us out, we pray you! Our prison is so dark and gloomy, will you not free us?"

The maiden was astonished. Should she free whatever was inside? As she was trying to make up her mind, she heard Epimetheus coming again. She knew he would not let her peep, but would tie up the box, so she hurriedly lifted up the lid to look inside before he came.

Alas! Within the box were crammed all the sorrows, pains, and evils of the world! As soon as Pandora lifted the lid, out they all flew, tiny brown-winged creatures like moths. They flew to Pandora and the surprised Epimetheus, and stung them. At once the two felt pain and anger for the first time. Then the brown-winged creatures flew out into the forest, and fastening themselves on to the merry-makers there, changed their cries of happiness to pain and dismay.

Epimetheus and Pandora began to quarrel. Pandora wept bitterly, and Epimetheus scolded her angrily for opening the box. In the midst of their quarrel, they suddenly heard a sweet voice calling to them. They stopped their angry words to listen.

The voice came from the box, which Pandora had hurriedly shut as soon as the brown-winged creatures had flown out. It was a high voice, sweet and loving.

"Let met out, let me out!" it cried. "I will heal your

sorrows, and bring you peace! Only let me out!"

"Shall I open the box again?" said Pandora.

"Since you cannot do much worse mischief than you have done already, you may as well see what is left," said Epimetheus gloomily.

So for the second time Pandora opened the box, and this time out flew, not a brown-winged creature, but a little snowy-winged spirit. She was called Hope, and had been crammed in at the bottom of all the evil creatures. It was her duty to heal the wounds made by them, and to cheer up those whom they had visited.

She flew at once to Pandora and Epimetheus and, brushing the wounds on their skin with her snowy wings, she healed them. Then off she flew to do the same for their unhappy companions outside.

And thus, because of Pandora's foolish curiosity, sorrow, pain, and evil entered the world, and have been with us ever since. But Hope stayed too, and while we have her, we are content.

Phaeton and the Sun-Horses

In a sunny corner of Greece there once dwelt a lovely nymph called Clymene. She had a golden-haired son, Phaeton, and when the yellow sunshine played on his hair, she would laugh and say:

"See how your father caresses you, Phaeton!"

"Is my father then the great sun-god?" asked the little boy. "Is it he who drives the golden sun-chariot across the sky, each day?"

"It is indeed he," answered Clymene. "You may well be proud of such a father, Phaeton."

The boy was pleased to think that his father was a god. He ran out to tell his playmates. At first they believed him, and listened in wonder. But as the days went by and Phaeton boasted more and more of his wonderful father, his friends became tired.

"Show us some proof that he is indeed your father," they cried. "We do not believe you, Phaeton. You are a boaster!"

White with anger, the boy ran to his mother.

"They say that the great Apollo is not my father!" he said. "Mother, let me go to him, and ask him to show these unbelievers that I am indeed his son."

"You shall go," said Clymene fondly. "I will tell you

the way, and you shall set forth tomorrow."

The next day the boy set out on his long journey. Eagerly he set his face to the east, where the great sun-chariot appeared each morning. Day after day he walked steadily towards Apollo's palace, eager to meet his father and embrace him.

At last he arrived, and stood marveling at the wonderful palace, whose pillars glittered with gold and precious stones, whose ceilings were of ivory, and whose doors were of gleaming silver.

The boy climbed the golden steps to the throne-room, and stopped on the threshold, dazzled by the brightness within. Apollo sat on his glittering throne, with his crown of gleaming sun-rays on his bright head.

Seeing the boy, he took off his crown, and laid it aside,

bidding the youth come near him.

"I am your son," said Phaeton proudly. "I come to greet you, oh my father. My playmates scoff at me, and say that I am not your son. I would have you prove it to them, so that I may not feel shame before them."

"You are indeed my son," said Apollo, holding out his arms to the boy, who gladly went to them. "I am your father and all the world shall know, for I will prove it to every one. Ask me anything you wish, and I will grant it."

"Father, grant that I may drive your sun-chariot tomorrow!" cried Phaeton, delighted to hear what his father said. "Then when my friends on the earth below see me holding the reins, they will look up in wonder and say: 'See! There is Phaeton in his father's chariot! Now we know that he spoke the truth.'"

A frown darkened the god's forehead, and he shook his head.

"Ask me anything but that, Phaeton, my son," he said. "The horses cannot be guided by any hand but mine. Even stern Jupiter, chief of all the gods, dares not drive my chariot. You do not know what you ask. Choose another wish, and I will grant it."

"I will have nothing else," said the willful boy, beginning to pout and frown. "A god cannot break his word, my father, and I hold you to yours. Let me drive the sun-horses."

Nothing that Apollo could say would make the boy change his mind, and at last the sun-god gave his consent.

"You will kill yourself," he said. "You are foolish to pay no heed to my warning, but since you will not choose any other favor, I cannot help but grant your wish. See, dawn is near at hand, and the gates of heaven are opening. It is time to mount the sun-chariot, and set forth on the journey through the heavens."

Apollo led his son to the gleaming chariot. The four horses were harnessed to the chariot-pole, and eagerly they pawed the ground, and champed their bits, anxious to be off.

Phaeton leapt into the car and took the reins, while Apollo gave him solemn warning.

"Drive along the middle way of the sky," he said, "for the middle course is the safest. If you go too low, you will set the mountain-tops on fire, and if you go too high you will lose your way among the stars. Do not use the whip, for the horses need holding in rather than urging on. Even my strong hand is hardly powerful enough to grasp the reins firmly. As for yours, my son, I fear that it will never hold in such fiery horses – leap down now, I pray you, and let me take your place. It is not too late to change your mind."

But the proud boy would not heed his father's warning. He took the reins impatiently, and the horses leapt forward. In a moment they were gone.

At first Phaeton remembered all his father had told him. He held the reins tightly, and called the horses by name. But soon the fiery animals felt that the hand holding them was not the strong one to which they were accustomed. They pulled at the reins, and Phaeton could not hold the horses back.

Then they ran wild among the stars, leaving the road they knew, and plunged madly here and there. Phaeton

was terrified, and the people on the earth below gazed upwards in horror, frightened to see the sun traveling out of his usual course.

The boy pulled at the reins with all his might. He tried to call to the horses, but so great was his fear that he could not remember their names. He dropped the reins and sank to his knees, holding fearfully to the chariot, which was rocking from side to side.

Then the sun-horses left the stars, and plunged downwards towards the earth. The chariot grazed the mountain-tops and set them on fire. So great was the heat that rivers were dried up, seas grew less, and trees withered and died. Nearer and nearer to the earth went the chariot, and all the people cried out in fear.

The fruitful ground was scorched and withered in great stretches, which became deserts that remain to this day.

The terrified people fell upon their knees and prayed to Jupiter to save them. All their crops were destroyed, and every blade of grass was withered. The very lakes boiled and seethed with the heat, and here and there the earth itself cracked and groaned.

Jupiter heard the cries from the frightened people. Rising from his couch, he looked out through the heavens to see what the tumult was about. When he saw the smoking earth, and caught sight of the sun-chariot plunging downwards, he knew that only he could save the world.

He took a thunderbolt, and hurled it fiercely at the chariot. It struck Phaeton on the shoulder, and he fell to

earth, his hair ablaze.

Then the sun-horses shook off their yokes, and broke loose. They galloped off to find their stalls in the sky, and that day night came early, for the sun shone no more after midday.

In vain Clymene and Apollo grieved for their foolish little son. He was slain by the thunderbolt, and fell into the river Eridanus. His friend Cygnus dived in to find him, but at last pined away in sorrow, and was turned into a swan. For many a year he swam up and down the waters, mourning for the golden-haired Phaeton.

Proserpina and the King of the Underworld

There was once a beautiful maiden called Proserpina, who loved to play with the nymphs among the flowers. Her mother, Ceres, was the goddess of agriculture, and worked hard to make the farmer's corn grow well. Often she left her little daughter in the care of the nymphs all day long, but at night, when she returned from her labors, she took Proserpina lovingly in her arms and kissed her, for she loved her daughter better than anything else in the world.

One day Proserpina went to gather flowers with her playmates, the nymphs. She sat on a bank making bright garlands, laughing her silvery laugh, and singing merry songs. The nymphs sat around her, filling her lap with fresh violets.

Suddenly there came the sound of galloping hoofs in the distance, and the nymphs looked to see who drove the horses – but they saw nothing, for trees and bushes hid the nearby carriage.

The dark driver of the galloping horses heard the songs and laughter of the maiden Proserpina. He longed to see who the singer was, so he pulled in his four coal-black horses, leapt down from his carriage, and went to peep through the bushes.

He was Pluto, King of the Underworld, a dark and gloomy monarch, feared by everyone. No flowers blossomed in his horrid kingdom, no birds sang, and the sun never shone. His face was stern, and his lips set tightly together, for he never smiled. On his dark head he wore a crown, and in his hand he carried a scepter and a key, to show how carefully he guarded those he took with him to his underground kingdom.

As soon as he saw the beautiful maiden Proserpina sitting happily among the flowers, he fell in love with her, and longed to take her down to his dark kingdom to brighten it. He knew that her mother, Ceres, would never let her marry him, so he made up his mind to capture her right away, and carry her off.

He strode through the bushes, and made his way to the surprised maiden. The nymphs leapt up in terror, for they knew Pluto. He caught hold of Proserpina, and picked her up. She screamed and dropped all her flowers in panic, calling for her mother to come and help her.

Pluto knew that if Ceres came he would certainly be forced to let the maiden go, so he ran swiftly to his waiting carriage, leapt into it with Proserpina, shook the reins, and galloped off with her. The black horses rushed away, and soon the frightened maiden could no longer hear the cries and wails of her friends the nymphs.

"Set me free!" she begged. "Let me go back to my

mother, who will mourn for me bitterly, for she loves me with all her heart."

"And so do I love you with all my heart," said the dark king tenderly. "I want you to be my queen, fair Proserpina.

You shall sit by my side in my dismal kingdom, and brighten the darkness with your youth and beauty."

But Proserpina was frightened and unhappy. She struggled to get free, and cried aloud for help. Pluto held her tightly, and urged his horses on ever more swiftly. At last they came to the river Cyane, which, hearing the maiden's cries, reared up its waters angrily, as if it would engulf Pluto and his horses.

The king saw that it would be folly to enter the raging waters, and he struck the earth fiercely with his two-pronged spear. At once a yawning cavern appeared, down which the horses plunged. Proserpina cried out with fear, and then, thinking to leave something to show her mother the way she had gone, she quickly tore off her shining waistband and flung it to the water-nymph in the river, bidding her take it to Ceres.

Then the earth closed up, and nothing more was seen of Pluto and his black horses. Only the sound of their galloping feet could be heard echoing far beneath the ground. Not for a moment did the fiery animals pause until they reached the foot of Pluto's throne.

That night Ceres came home from her labors to seek her little daughter. She searched everywhere, and began to weep in fear, when she found the spilled flowers that Proserpina had dropped. She called her by name, but no one answered. All night long the poor mother sought for her daughter, and when day dawned she still wandered on, calling aloud for her.

Day after day Ceres journeyed to find Proserpina. She forgot her duties, and neglected to help the farmers. Grass and corn drooped, and fruit would not ripen. All over the world went the unhappy mother, asking for news of her child, but hearing none.

At last in despair she came back to the land from which she had first set out. She wandered by the banks of the river Cyane, and suddenly the waters cast a shining waistband at her feet. She picked it up with joy – for it was Proserpina's!

"Now I know that my child has been here!" she cried. "I shall find her if I seek long enough."

She hastened on, and soon came to a clear fountain, whose crystal waters gushed up into the air. Ceres sat down by them, weary with her search, and closing her eyes, she listened to the murmuring of the waters.

But suddenly she heard words in the murmuring. The fountain was speaking to her.

"Oh, Ceres, listen to me!" said the nymph of the fountain. "I grieve for you, for I have seen you weep for your daughter. I can tell you where she is."

"Tell me, tell me," begged Ceres.

"I draw my waters from dark caverns underground," murmured the nymph. "One day as I rushed along below the earth, I passed near the throne of gloomy Pluto, King of the Underworld. By his side I saw your fair daughter, Proserpina. She is his queen, oh Ceres, but she is not happy, for she longs for sunshine and

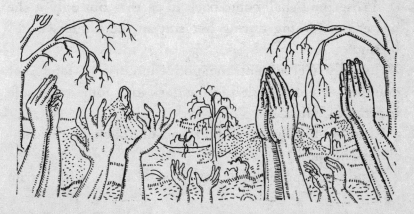

flowers, the song of birds and the laughter of friends."

Ceres listened in dismay. She was glad to know at last where her child was, but she knew that Pluto would never give her up. Mourning deeply, she went to a cave, and there she wept and sorrowed unseen, forgetting all her duties to men and women.

"Nothing shall grow on the earth while my daughter is with Pluto," she vowed. "The world shall mourn with me!"

Then trees and grass died, corn rotted, fruit perished. Hunger came among the people, and at last, almost starving, they prayed to Jupiter, King of Heaven, to bring back Proserpina, so that Ceres might once more be happy, and look after their crops for them.

When Ceres heard the prayers of the people she arose and left her cave. She too prayed to Jupiter to allow her daughter to return once more.

Then Jupiter, moved by so many prayers, granted Ceres' wish.

"Proserpina shall come back to earth – but only if she has eaten nothing during her stay in the Underworld," he said.

Joyfully Ceres sent the god Mercury to fetch her daughter. He descended to the dark kingdom, and made his way to Pluto.

"Jupiter bids you send Proserpina back to the sunshine," he said.

"And what more did he say?" asked Pluto, with a grim look.

"Only that if she had eaten anything she could not come," answered Mercury. "But it is well known that Proserpina has refused all food since she has been with you."

Then the bright-haired queen began to weep and wail bitterly. She held out a pomegranate to Mercury, and showed him where she had sucked some seeds from it.

"Alas! Alas!" she cried. "Only today have I accepted from Pluto this pomegranate, oh Mercury. I have eaten six seeds. Must I therefore stay here for ever?"

Mercury sadly made his way back to Jupiter, who sat frowning deeply.

"Return to the Underworld," he commanded Mercury. "Tell Pluto that for every seed Proserpina has eaten, she must stay for a month with him – the rest of the year she may spend with her mother on earth."

Swiftly Mercury returned to Pluto, and gave him Jupiter's message.

"She has eaten six seeds, therefore she must spend six months of each year with me," said the dark king. "I have been kind to her, so she should return willingly to me when the time comes."

Gladly Proserpina arose from her throne, and went to Mercury's side. He carried her up the long, dark way to the sunshine, and there, eager and loving, stood Ceres, her mother, her arms outstretched in welcome.

Proserpina ran to her, and embraced her, overjoyed to

see her again. Then the whole world rejoiced with Ceres. The sun shone warmly down, and the clouds fled away. The grass sprang up bright and fresh, new wheat made the fields green, flowers bloomed, and birds sang.

For six months Proserpina lived with her mother, happy and free from care, playing every day in the bright sunshine. Men and women rejoiced, for the world

was fruitful, and when harvest-time came, the granaries were full to overflowing.

But as the half-year drew to an end, the thoughts of Proserpina turned to gloomy Pluto, all alone in his dark kingdom. She knew that he missed her, and longed for her return, for in his own stern and frowning way he loved her dearly.

"I must go now to Pluto," she told her mother, when the six months ended. "Do not grieve, for the King of the Underworld is not unkind to me. I will return again to you at the end of another half-year."

She went back to Pluto – but Ceres again withdrew to her cave, and wept and sorrowed for all the months that Proserpina was away. And once again the world sorrowed with her, the flowers died, the birds ceased their singing, and clouds shut out the golden sun.

Year after year the same thing happened. All was sunshine and brightness when Proserpina appeared, and sorrow and darkness when she went. So we have the beauty and warmth of summer, when the daughter of Ceres is with us, and the cold and bitterness of winter when she has departed. The world rejoices at her return, and mourns when she is gone.

The Maiden of the Laurel Tree

One day, as Apollo walked through the forest, he saw Cupid, the little God of Love, playing with his bow and arrows. He stopped by him, and laughed.

"Why do you play with such warlike weapons?" he asked. "Leave such things to me, little god. What harm can you do with those?"

"You cannot harm me with *your* weapons, but I can harm you with mine," answered Cupid. He chose a sharp-pointed, golden arrow, and fitting it to his bow, shot it at Apollo. Then he chose a second arrow, blunt and tipped with lead. This he shot at a lovely maiden, Daphne, the daughter of the river-god.

As soon as the golden arrow struck Apollo he became full of love for Daphne, but she, struck by the leaden arrow, would have none of his wooing. In vain he pleaded with her to marry him; she would not let him come near her.

She was a strong maiden, fair of face, and fond of running and hunting. She wished to marry no one, least of all Apollo. When he fell upon his knees, and begged her to show him mercy, she ran away.

Then Apollo, fierce and full of love, pursued her. She did not fear him at first, for she thought that she could easily outrun him – but soon she saw that he would overtake her, for he was very strong and tireless.

"Do not fly from me!" begged Apollo. "I am no peasant fellow, lovely Daphne. I am Apollo, god of the sun, strong and powerful. Marry me, and we will be happy together."

But Daphne was deaf to his cries. On she went, and on and on, panting and fearful. Then, glancing round, she saw that the god had almost caught her up.

Poor Daphne could not run much longer. Swiftly she turned and fled down to the river, calling upon her father to help her.

"Oh, my father!" she cried. "Save me, save me! Change my form, so that Apollo will not know me! I can run no further!"

The river-god heard her call. Quickly he rose from the

waters, and muttered the words that would save his daughter from Apollo.

Then a strange thing happened. The maiden felt her feet rooted to the ground so that she could no longer move them. Her outstretched arms became branches, and round her soft body grew the bark of a tree. Her hair and fingers became leaves waving in the wind – she was changed to a laurel tree!

Apollo came rushing up, and flung his arms around her – then he drew back in surprise. It was no maiden he was embracing, but a tree. Soon he saw what had happened, and in grief he kissed the tree, and called it by loving names.

"Sweet Daphne!" he said. "You should not have been so fearful of me. I would not have harmed you. But since you are now lost to me for ever, and cannot be my bride, you shall be my tree. I will wear a crown of your leaves, and when men are crowned conquerors they too shall choose your leaves for wreaths. Both men and gods shall pay you homage. Your leaves shall always be green, and shall never decay!"

So to this day the laurel is evergreen, and, as Apollo promised, its leaves are always chosen for the crowns of conquerors.

The Watchman with a Hundred Eyes

Once Jupiter, King of Heaven, saw a lovely maiden called Io, daughter of the river-god. He admired her very much and came down to earth to visit her. He was afraid that Juno, his wife, would be jealous, and so that she might not see him talking to Io, he caused a thick cloud to hide them from sight.

But one afternoon, Juno, awaking from sleep, looked out from her high window in heaven. She had that day commanded all the clouds to leave the earth, and when she saw one by the river, thick and unmoving, she was

filled with wonder.

She descended to earth to find out what made it. Jupiter heard her coming and, swift as thought, changed the river-nymph into a lovely heifer. When Juno swept away the cloud, all she saw was Jupiter by the side of a beautiful cow.

"Why do you need this cloud?" she asked.

"See, I have been creating a lovely heifer," said Jupiter. "Is she not pretty?"

Juno wondered if the heifer had been a nymph. "I will ask Jupiter to give her to me; then if he refuses I shall know that it is no heifer, but a nymph," she thought.

Jupiter did not want to give Juno the heifer, but he could think of no reason to refuse his wife's request. So he handed the heifer over to her, and Juno took her.

She called her watchman, Argus, and when he came she bade him watch over the heifer carefully, and guard her so well that Jupiter could not take her away again. Argus promised to obey, and at once sat down by the heifer to watch.

There was no better watchman in the world than Argus, for he had a hundred eyes, and these were never all closed at once. Only one pair was shut at a time, leaving ninety-eight on guard.

Poor Io, amazed at being turned into a heifer, tried to call her father and sisters to her. But her voice had changed to a loud bellow, and terrified her. Her father

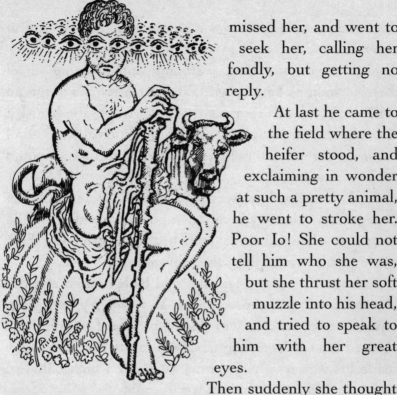

missed her, and went to seek her, calling her fondly, but getting no reply.

At last he came to the field where the heifer stood, and exclaiming in wonder at such a pretty animal, he went to stroke her. Poor Io! She could not tell him who she was, but she thrust her soft muzzle into his head, and tried to speak to him with her great eyes.

Then suddenly she thought that she would write her name in the earth with her hoof. It was such a short name that she could easily do that. So she stretched out her hoof and scraped her name in the earth – Io, she wrote, and then Io, again.

Her father looked to see what the heifer was doing and as soon as he saw her name written there, he guessed what had happened. He embraced the heifer sadly, and when her sisters came running up, he told them the pretty animal was no other than their beautiful sister Io.

Now Argus had been watching and listening to all this. As soon as he learned that the heifer was a nymph called Io, he sent the news to Juno. When she heard it she was very angry, and bade Argus watch the heifer all the more carefully, for she felt certain that Jupiter would try to rescue her.

Jupiter, meanwhile, was very unhappy. He could not bear to think that the lovely nymph was a heifer, and he longed to change her back to her own form. But how could he outwit Argus of the hundred eyes?

At last he sent for Mercury, and bade him go and put the watchman to sleep, and then slay him. Mercury hastened to obey, taking with him a bunch of poppies. He dressed himself as a shepherd, and in the heat of midday made his way to where Argus sat upon a high bank, so that he could see all the country round.

Argus was very dull. No one came near him, and he longed for company. When he saw the shepherd coming, he called out to him.

"Ho there, shepherd! Come and sit down on this bank with me!"

Mercury did so. Then he began to tell merry stories to Argus, and to sing him tuneful songs. But these kept the watchman more wide awake than ever. Not one of his hundred eyes closed.

Then Mercury began to tell him a long tale, dull and boring. Argus yawned, and closed two of his eyes. The sun was very hot, and everything was very quiet. Only Mercury's voice went on and on, like a murmuring stream.

Argus tried to listen, but he was too sleepy. Two more of his eyes closed, and then two more. He yawned more widely than ever, and when he had finished yawning, Mercury saw that ten of his eyes were now closed tightly.

The story-teller droned on and on. Argus closed more and more of his eyes, and at last lay back on the grass. Mercury bent over him, and saw that about twenty of his eyes were still wide open, keeping a watch on Io. He went on with his long, dull tale, often repeating himself, until he saw that ninety-eight of Argus's eyes were fast closed, and only two were open.

But these two were very bright and wide awake. No matter how hard Mercury tried, he could not get them to close. They shone steadily, following every movement of Io's.

Then, taking his bunch of poppies, Mercury shook them over the watchman's head. The magic in them caused Argus to be so full of sleep that even his last pair of eyes felt heavy and dull. He longed to close them, but for a long while he would not. Then at last Mercury saw them closing – Argus was fast asleep, and all his hundred eyes were shut.

Swiftly he slew the sleeping watchman. Then, taking the heifer's rope, he led her away to Jupiter, who gladly changed her back again to her right form. The poor maiden was overjoyed to be herself once more, but for a long time she did not dare to speak, being fearful lest she should bellow.

That evening Juno came to see Argus. When she found him lying dead, she was full of sorrow. She took his hundred eyes, and placed them in her peacock's tail, in memory of her faithful guard; and there they are to this day for everyone to see.

The Story of Echo and Narcissus

Echo was a lovely nymph, who was so fond of the sound of her own voice that she seldom stopped talking. One day she met the goddess Juno, and talked so much to her that she was rebuked for chattering. Echo answered the goddess rudely, and angered her. "For punishment you shall lose your voice!" said Juno. "You shall never speak again except to repeat the last words of others! Go and hide yourself away among the hills, and do not dare to come forth and show yourself until someone bids you do so!"

Echo ran away in dismay. When she tried to speak she found that her voice was gone. It was only when she heard others talking that she could say anything – and even then she could say nothing but the last word she heard.

One day there came to the hills a beautiful youth called Narcissus. His body was straight and white, and his face was fairer than any nymph's. His black hair curled over his broad forehead, and his bright eyes sparkled and shone. Echo peeped from behind a tree and saw him.

At once she fell in love with him, and longed for him to love her. But how could she show herself to him, for Juno had forbidden her to come forth from her hiding-place unless someone bade her do so.

Echo followed the beautiful youth up the mountain. He heard a rustling noise behind him, and stopped. He looked round, but could see no one. On he went again – but soon stopped once more, certain that someone was following him.

"Who is there?" he cried.

"There!" answered Echo, repeating his last word.

"Who are you?" asked the youth, seeing no one.

"You!" answered Echo.

"Do not mock me!" cried Narcissus angrily.

"Me!" said poor Echo.

"Come forth and show yourself here!" commanded Narcissus.

"Here!" Echo answered gladly, and stepped forth in all her loveliness. But Narcissus was angry. He was very vain, and thought that Echo had mocked him. He paid no heed to her loving looks, and when she put her arms round him, he pushed her roughly away.

"I heard you mocking me!" he said angrily. "Why do

you pretend to love me? You are only making fun of me, and no doubt your friends are behind the trees, laughing. Go away!"

Sadly Echo obeyed him, murmuring, "Away!" as she glided between the trees, wishing with all her heart that the proud youth might himself love in vain, and know what pain it was.

Narcissus went on his way up the mountain. Soon he felt thirsty, and coming to a clear pool, he lay down to drink from it. Suddenly he saw in the water the reflection of his own beautiful face – but he thought it was a nymph looking up at him from the pool, and right away he fell in love with his own reflection.

"Sweet nymph, beautiful nymph, will you not come from your pool and play with me?" he begged. The lovely face in the water moved its lips as he moved his –

but Narcissus could hear no sound coming from them.
He stretched out his arms into the pool, but no sooner
did they touch the surface of the water than the lovely
face vanished.

He waited patiently until the water became smooth
again, and then once more he leaned over. He smiled at
the face below, and was overjoyed to see it smile back.
He spoke again, and saw the lips move with his. But
plead as he might, the nymph would not come from the
pool.

Echo, seeing him talking to someone in the water,
peeped over his shoulder to see who it might be. When
she saw that there was only his own reflection there, she
longed to tell him that he had fallen in love with himself.
But she could not, for she could only repeat his last
words. Then she became very sad, for she saw that her
wish had come true – Narcissus loved in vain, for his
reflection could never return the fondness he showed it.

The poor youth would not leave the pool. In vain he
begged the nymph to come forth, in vain he smiled and
stretched out his arms. All day long he lay there, and all
night, for when the bright moon rode in the sky, he saw
his reflection clearly, and spoke to it lovingly.

Days went by, and still Narcissus lay by the water. He
neither ate nor drank, for he had forgotten everything
save his love for the nymph in the pool. He wept tears
into the water, but when he found that they sent away

his reflection, and broke it up, he wept no more. He could not bear the nymph to go away.

Soon he grew thin and pale, and the nymph in the water did likewise. Narcissus was very unhappy; Echo too was miserable, for she knew that he would soon die – but she could say nothing to warn him.

One morning, when the sun rose, the beautiful youth lay pale and dead. So white he was and so lovely as he lay there by the pool, that the gods themselves wept for him and his hopeless love. In pity they changed his body into a flower as white and lovely as himself – the little narcissus that loves to grow by the side of water.

And still the flower bends over to look at itself in the pools, even as Narcissus leaned over to gaze at his own reflection long years ago.

As for the poor nymph Echo, she pined away in sorrow, until there was nothing left of her but a voice. You may hear her still, among the hills, repeating your last words – but never again will she be seen.

The King with the Golden Touch

Midas, the richest king in the world, sat on his throne, thinking of his treasure-house. He longed to be richer still; he wished to have so much gold that no one could count it. But no matter how deeply he thought, he could find no way by which he might make himself still richer.

As he sat there thinking and planning, some shepherds came into the hall, and bowed low before the king. With them they brought an old man, Silenus.

"Lord," said the shepherds. "We found this old man wandering in your orchard. He is lost."

"It is Silenus, friend of the god Bacchus!" said Midas. He descended from his throne, and welcomed the old man. "You shall stay with me in my palace for ten days," he said. "I will feast you, and treat you well, and then I will take you back to your friend Bacchus."

So for ten days Silenus stayed with Midas and feasted royally. At the end of that time the king himself guided the old man back to the court of Bacchus.

The god was overjoyed to see his friend once more, for he had mourned him as lost. He embraced him, and then turned in gratitude to Midas.

"Ask what you will, and I will grant it," he promised.

Midas could hardly believe his ears. At last his chance had come! He could be richer than all the kings in the world put together!

"Grant that everything I touch shall be turned to gold!" he begged. "Let me have the Golden Touch!"

"So be it!" said Bacchus, laughing. "But do you think that will bring you happiness, Midas?"

"I know it will," answered the greedy king. "Oh, Bacchus, would you really grant this desire of mine?"

"The Golden Touch is yours!" said Bacchus, and turned to enter his palace.

Midas went homewards, followed by his wondering slaves. He longed to try his power, so he plucked a twig from a tree. Lo and behold! It turned to pure gold in his hands! Then the king knew that his wish had been granted, and he was beside himself with joy.

He touched his garments – they turned to glittering gold! But they felt very heavy, and the king could hardly walk. That did not trouble him, for he knew that they were now worth far more than before.

Then Midas stooped and picked up some common pebbles on the path. As he touched them, they too turned to bright yellow gold. The king handed them to his gaping slaves and bade them carry them. Then he touched a clod of earth, which at once changed to the precious metal. In a short time the slaves were so heavily laden with gold objects that they could hardly walk along.

Soon Midas came back to his own palace. As he passed through the gardens, he plucked a red rose. To his great delight it became a perfect golden blossom. It had lost its beautiful fragrance and softness, but what did Midas care for that? Was it not gold?

He pulled apples from the trees, and threw them to his attendants to place in the treasure-house. He changed a whole tree to gold, by passing his hands over the trunk and branches. There it stood, bright yellow, very stiff and very ugly; but Midas thought it was the most beautiful tree he had ever seen.

He entered his palace, and threw himself down on a seat, tired with excitement. At once the seat became solid gold, too heavy to move.

"Bring me water to wash with," commanded Midas. "And set the table with food, for I am hungry and would eat."

Slaves brought him a silver ewer of clear, cool water.

Midas turned the silver gold at a touch. Then he put his hands into the water.

At once it changed to golden ice! Midas could not wash his hands, and hastily he took them out of the curiously changed water. He sat down at the table, and saw with pleasure that the cloth, dishes, and glasses all turned to gold under his hands.

But now a great shock awaited the king. As soon as he put bread to his mouth, he found that that, too, turned to gold, and was uneatable! He snatched at a cake, and crammed it into his mouth quickly, hoping that he could swallow it before it became hard; but he could not. His teeth crunched on a golden cake, and he could neither bite nor swallow it.

The poor king took up a goblet of wine, and raised it to his mouth. He took a long draught, but even as it passed down his throat, it turned into a burning golden liquid, and Midas suddenly felt very ill.

He sat there, gazing at the fine food spread out before him, unable to eat a crumb. Soon his hunger overcame him again, and once more he tried to eat. The fish he took on his fork became stiff and golden, and the miserable king flung it down in dismay.

He arose, and went walking in the gardens, trying to forget his hunger. A slave approached him, but the king bade him go away, pushing him as he gave his command. At once the man became a golden statue, and stood stiffly on the grass unable to move or speak.

Midas was horrified, but he could not bring the man back to life again. As he stood there gazing in dismay at his golden slave, his children came running to him. Without thinking what he was doing, the king put his arms around them, only to find, to his great fear and horror, that they, like the slave, had all changed to little statues.

Then Midas was indeed unhappy. Could he, the richest man in the world, never eat or drink again? Were his beautiful children to remain golden statues? Was he to die of starvation, when by his magic power he could make enough gold to buy up all the corn, all the wine, in the world?

In despair, the wretched king fondled his golden children, and besought them to speak to him again, to look at  him with their merry eyes. The little golden statues said never a word.

Then Midas ran through the gardens, and went all alone down the highway. He meant to go to the god Bacchus, and beg him to take away this dreadful

Golden Touch. He walked as swiftly as he could, weighted down by his heavy golden garments, and at last, just as the sun was setting, he came to the court of the merry god Bacchus.

"Why do you return to me?" asked the god. "Have you not obtained the wish you asked?"

"Yes," answered Midas. "I have the Golden Touch, oh Bacchus! But I come now to ask you to remove it from me, for I am very unhappy. I can neither eat nor drink, and my beloved children are changed to golden statues."

"Did I not say that no happiness could come from the Golden Touch?" demanded the god. "Keep your gift, Midas, and do not come whining to me."

Then the frightened king fell upon his knees, and with golden tears rolling down his cheeks, besought Bacchus to be merciful.

"I was wrong to love gold so much," he cried. "I am bitterly punished. Pardon me, Bacchus, and remove this hateful gift from me. What can I do to cure myself?"

Then the god was sorry for the unhappy king. "Go to the waters of the river Pactolus," he said. "Bathe yourself therein, and the Golden Touch will leave you."

Midas hardly waited to thank the god, but at once made his way to the river. He plunged into the cool waters, and saw that they became amber yellow. He felt the mysterious power leaving him, and rejoiced.

When he came out of the river, he found that the

sandy bed had changed from silver to gold. To this day it has remained yellow, and even now men still pick up golden grains at the spot where the unhappy king bathed.

As soon as he came from the water, Midas touched the twig of a tree. He gazed on it fearfully, dreading to see it change to gold. But to his great joy it remained green and leafy.

"Now may Bacchus be praised!" he said. "The Golden Touch has indeed left me!"

He touched the ground, and picked up many stones, but they did not change. He plucked some ripening grapes from the hedge, and eagerly put them in his mouth. They remained soft and juicy, and with delight the king ate them, for he was very hungry.

Then he remembered his golden children and his golden slave. Tears sprang to his eyes, and rolled down his cheeks, but this time they were real tears, not golden ones. He borrowed a pitcher from a nearby cottage and filled it with water from the river. Then he ran to his palace.

He emptied the water over his children and his slave. To his joy they came alive once more. The king embraced his children lovingly, and then, happy once again, turned to go with them into the palace.

He sat down at the table, and looked around.

"Take these gold dishes away," he commanded. "Bring

me plain and common ones, for I sicken at the sight of gold."

In surprise his servants did his bidding. Then, taking his bread and meat from common dishes, the king ate the best meal he had ever tasted. The bread remained bread, the meat remained meat, and the wine remained wine.

Thus was Midas cured of his greed for gold, and learned that riches do not bring a man happiness or peace.

The Story of Orpheus and Eurydice

Orpheus loved two things, his lute and the sweet maiden Eurydice. With his lute he made such wonderful music that everything listened in delight. All the wild animals left their lairs, and crept about his knee, the birds flew around his head, and the trees bent nearer to listen. Even the rocks softened when they heard Orpheus playing on his lute.

Eurydice loved his music too. When he came to woo her, she listened to his songs with joy. Soon she promised to marry him, and when the wedding-day came the woods rang with happiness and mirth.

But alas for Eurydice! As she danced at her bridal feast, she trod upon a snake in the grass. It struck at her

in anger, and bit her foot. The maiden cried out in pain, and Orpheus ran to her.

But he could do nothing to help her. The snake was poisonous, and before night came, Eurydice was dead.

Then Orpheus was wild with grief. He went among the woods and hills, playing such mournful music on his lute that everything wept to hear him. He could not live without Eurydice, and at last he went to Jupiter, begging him to let him go down to the Underworld, where the gloomy King Pluto reigned.

"There I shall see my lovely Eurydice!" he said. "Let me go, oh Jupiter, for life is nothing to me without her."

"Go then," said Jupiter, "but the way is strewn with perils, Orpheus. Think twice before you venture into

Pluto's dread kingdom."

Orpheus turned to go, his heart lighter for the first time since Eurydice's death. He made his way to the black river Styx, and begged the ferryman, Charon, to ferry him across to the Underworld.

At first Charon would not, but when Orpheus began to play on his lute, he consented. Then, with sweet music in his ears, old Charon for the first time rowed a living man across the dark river.

Orpheus landed on the opposite shore. He went to the entrance of Pluto's kingdom, and there, lying by the mouth of the cave that led to the Underworld, was Cerberus, a fierce, three-headed monster. His duty it was to guard the entrance, and to see that nothing living passed in, and to forbid any dead spirit to pass out.

When he saw Orpheus, he made as if he would spring upon him and devour him. But the lute-player played

such sad and enchanting music that the dreadful dog lay down and let him pass by in peace.

Through the caves Orpheus went, still playing on his lute. The spirits in the Underworld heard the sweet music, and came crowding round him to listen. Orpheus paid no heed to any of them. He had come to seek his beloved Eurydice, and her only did he desire.

Soon he passed by the wicked daughters of Danaus, who had killed their husbands on their wedding night. For this they were punished by being forced to fill a bottomless cask. This they could not do, but if they paused for a moment, a lash fell upon their shoulders, and they hurried to fetch more water. When they heard the lovely music of Orpheus, they rested in their hopeless task, and for a few moments tasted delight again.

Near by was the wicked King Tantalus. He stood up to his chin in pure, clear water, and over his head hung a luscious bunch of sweet grapes. The king was tormented by a fearful hunger and thirst, but whenever he stooped to drink the water, it fled away from him, and if he put up his hand to the grapes, they swung out of his reach.

As Orpheus passed by, Tantalus for the first time forgot his hunger and thirst, and turned to listen to the lovely music. But Orpheus did not see him. Always he strained his eyes for Eurydice, striving to catch a glimpse of her sweet form among the shadows.

Soon the lute-player came to a steep hill, where the

evil king Sisyphus was condemned to roll a great stone up to the top. But when he had just reached the summit the stone always slipped from his grasp, and rolled to the bottom. Then Sisyphus had to climb down and roll it up again.

When Orpheus came by, Sisyhus paused in his dismal task, and looked round in amazement to hear such sweet sounds in the Underworld. He sat down upon his stone, and for a little while forgot his woes in listening to the music. But Orpheus passed him without heeding. On and on he went until he came to the very throne of Pluto.

There sat the dark king, and by his side was the lovely Proserpina, her bright face shining out from the shadows.

"Why do you come here, mortal?" demanded Pluto. "Do you not know that only the dead pass through the portals of my kingdom?"

"Oh Pluto," sang Orpheus, "I come to find my sweet love Eurydice. Without her there is no life for me. You took her from me while she was too young – we had but just began our happiness together. Give her back to me again, for I love her. Do you not remember, oh Pluto, how you fetched Proserpina from the world above? Have you forgotten the love you felt for her then? I, in my turn, would fetch my love Eurydice from this world below. Oh, give her to me once again, or keep me here with you, for I will not live without her!"

As Pluto and Proserpina listened to the mournful song of Orpheus, tears sprang to their eyes. All the listening spirits sighed dolefully, and the air was full of soft groans. Proserpina leaned towards Pluto and whispered beseechingly to him.

Pluto nodded, and then turned to Orpheus.

"Your wish is granted," he said. "Go back the way you came, mortal, and Eurydice shall follow behind you. But speak not on the way, nor pause. Do not look behind you, for if your eyes fall upon Eurydice before you reach the upper air, she will be lost to you forever!"

Then Orpheus, a great gladness in his heart, turned away from Pluto's throne. He swept the strings of his lute, and the music that came forth from them was like laughter itself – a strange sound in that dismal kingdom. He passed upwards towards the faint glimmer of light that showed the entrance to the upper world.

Behind him he heard the following steps of his love Eurydice. He heard her soft breathing, and joy filled his heart. He spoke no word, and made no pause. On he went and on, and ever behind him came the patter of Eurydice's small feet.

Then, just as he came near the outlet to the world of sunshine and life, Orpheus wondered whether the time she had spent in the Underworld had changed Eurydice in any way. Would she look pale and wan, would some of her sweet beauty have died?

Without thinking, the eager lover turned to gaze on the face of Eurydice – but no sooner had he turned than she sighed dolefully, and murmuring, "Farewell, a last farewell!" vanished from before his eyes. Down the long, dark passage she fled, and Orpheus stretched his arms out to the empty air.

Mad with grief, he tried to follow her, but he could not. He was led back to the world above, and there he wandered about with his lute, making such unhappy music that even the rocks wept to hear it.

At last he died, and then his spirit raced to meet Eurydice's. Gladly they embraced, and then, happy at last, wandered together in the lovely Elysian Fields, never more to be parted one from the other.

Clytie, the Sunflower Maiden

There was once a beautiful water-nymph called Clytie. She had wonderful golden hair, and every day she used to come forth from her pool and comb it. It fell around her face in great waves, and shone in the sun like gold.

Clytie loved the warmth of the sun. She used to watch for Apollo's chariot to come through the gates of heaven every morning. Then the world was flooded with the sunrise, and hills and valleys rejoiced.

One day Clytie saw Apollo driving the sun-chariot. He wore his dazzling crown, and his face shone fair and bright. He was strong and handsome, and held the reins of his four fiery horses firmly in his powerful hand.

Through the sky he went all day long, driving the horses along the middle way. Clytie watched him, and admired his strength and his beauty. She was sorry when the sun-chariot entered the western seas, and was lost to her. Darkness came over the earth, and Clytie shivered. She returned to the water, and dreamed of the bright young sun-god all night long.

The next morning she arose before dawn, and stood by the side of the pool, watching for the return of Apollo. Soon a golden light tinged the eastern sky, and

then the sun-god came forth once more. Clytie watched him eagerly. All day long she followed his course, sighing when he returned to the west.

The little nymph fell deeply in love with the handsome god. She thought of him and of nothing else. No longer did she return to her pool at night, but stood waiting in the darkness for the first golden gleam to appear in the east.

She longed for Apollo to see her, and to return her love. She felt certain that if he saw her waiting for him, he would come to her with loving words. So all day long she watched and waited for him to see her.

She combed out her pretty hair so that it hung round

her face like a sheet of gold. It gleamed in the sun, and shone so brightly that her sister nymphs came up to her and stroked her head. But Clytie paid no heed to them. Always she watched for the moment when Apollo would see her and smile.

But the sun-god did not turn his head. He looked straight before him, keeping his fiery horses on their difficult way. He did not see Clytie of the golden hair watching him with loving eyes.

Day after day the nymph saw Apollo drive out from the eastern sky, mount the heavens, and return to the western seas at night. Her face turned to him wherever he went and followed his course all day long.

For nine days Clytie watched the sun-god, and never once did she take her eyes from him. She had no food and no drink, save only her own bitter tears. Then, on the ninth day, when she would have moved, she could not.

Her feet had become rooted to the ground. Her arms and fingers were green leaves. Her face, with its halo of golden hair, had become a flower!

Clytie was a sunflower. She could neither speak nor weep; but still she turned her golden head towards the sun, following his course the whole day through. And from that time to this all sunflowers do the same – their pretty golden faces look always towards the sun-god, as he drives his golden chariot through the sky.

The Story of Baucis and Philemon

Once upon a time Jupiter and his son Mercury came down to visit the earth. They dressed themselves as ordinary travelers, and went to the land of Phrygia, where they came one evening to a little village.

They were tired and hungry, and were glad to see the lights in the cottages.

"Let us ask for food and shelter here," said Jupiter. "We will see what kind of folks these be."

As soon as they reached the village, the children came

out to see them. They shouted rudely at the strangers, and threw stones at them, while the dogs barked loudly, and made as if they would bite them.

Jupiter knocked at a cottage door, and when the woman came, he asked courteously if they might have food and shelter there. The women laughed in his face, and answered him rudely that they had enough to do to keep themselves without feeding strangers. She slammed the door, and left the travelers standing on the doorstep.

At cottage after cottage the gods found the same answer. None would help them, none would give them even a drink of water. Jupiter grew angry, and vowed that he would bring destruction on such a wicked village.

Soon they came to a tiny cottage set a little way up the hill. It had but one room, but the garden round was neat, and the thatch on the roof was well patched. The gods knocked at the door, and it was opened by an old woman, Baucis.

Baucis and her husband, Philemon, had lived in the little cottage ever since they had first married. They had always been happy together, and, unlike the rest of the villagers, they were kind-hearted and courteous.

The old woman welcomed the two travelers and bade them enter. Philemon placed a bench for them, and put a cushion stuffed with seaweed upon it. Baucis went to the fireplace, and kindled a fire. She placed the little kettle on some sticks, and promised to give the strangers warm water to wash in, as soon as the kettle boiled.

Philemon went into the neat garden, and plucked some pot-herbs. He took down the flitch of bacon that hung from the roof, and cut off a piece. Baucis put it and the herbs into the pot. Then she poured some hot water into a wooden bowl, and set it before her guests, inviting them to wash.

Although the strangers looked like ordinary travelers, the old woman felt that there was something unusual about them. She wanted to give them the very best she had – but, alas, she had so little!

She took out a very old and coarse cloth to spread upon the table. It was snowy white, and was only used on special days. She set some olives on the table, and some berries pickled in vinegar. Philemon pulled some radishes from the garden, and brought cheese from the cupboard. Some eggs were cooked in the hot ashes, and served in earthen dishes. Then the stew from the pot was ready, and the two strangers fell upon the simple meal with good appetite.

At the end of the feast Baucis produced some ripe apples and some wild honey, beaming with delight to see how heartily her guests enjoyed their meal.

For drink there was some new wine in a pitcher. The strangers were very thirsty, and drank a great deal. Baucis began to feel astonished that her old pitcher held so much wine. The guests drank cup after cup, and yet the pitcher always seemed full. How could that be?

The travelers filled up their cups again, and drank. Baucis and Philemon thought that surely the pitcher must be empty now. They peeped in to see – and, lo and behold! it was full of wine to the brim.

Then the old couple were terrified, for they knew that their guests were no ordinary men. They looked at them closely, and knew them to be Jupiter and Mercury. Full of fear and dismay, they fell upon their knees, and begged their visitors to pardon them for the poor meal they had offered them.

"We gave you the best we had," they said, "but our best is very poor, we know. Forgive us, lords, for the coarse fare we set before you!"

Suddenly Baucis remembered that they had an old goose, who guarded their cottage for them. She would kill that as a sacrifice to the gods! She whispered to Philemon, and the two old people went out to get the goose.

But the bird did not wish to be caught and killed. It used its feet and wings well, and, hissing and cackling, ran this way and that to get away from Baucis and Philemon. At last it ran between the knees of the two gods themselves, and stayed there.

"Do not slay your goose, old people," said Jupiter gently. "We are gods, as you have guessed. We are grateful to you for offering us food and shelter, when you had so little yourself. You shall be rewarded, but all the rest of the village shall be punished. Ask any wish from us, and it shall be granted."

Baucis took Philemon aside, and for a few moments the good pair whispered together. Amazement and delight were on their wrinkled old faces. The gods were not angry, but pleased!

"Grant that we may serve the gods well till we die," said Philemon, "and grant, oh great lords, that we may each die at the same moment, so that one may not be left to mourn the other. This is the wish we ask."

Jupiter smiled. He had expected Philemon to ask for something magnificent — a palace, wealth, youth, perhaps — but the old man's wish was so simple and small that the god marveled to hear it.

"Your wish shall be granted," he said. "Now come with me to the top of the hill, for I would show you something."

The old couple went panting up the hill with Jupiter and Mercury. When they reached the top, they saw a strange sight. All the village was sinking into a lake, and every villager was drowned. Only their own tiny cottage was left standing, and even as they looked at it, it changed.

The corner-posts turned into great columns, the brown thatch became a golden roof, the earth floors changed to marble. The door grew larger, and became a beautiful portal, carved and adorned with gold.

"It is a temple!" cried Philemon, in amazement. "See, wife – our little cottage is a temple!"

"You shall look after it, and serve the gods there, as you wished," said Jupiter. "You shall be known as keepers of the temple, and when strangers come to worship, they shall hear your story."

Then the gods vanished. Baucis and Philemon went down to the temple, and entered it. They kept it to the end of their lives, living there happily and contentedly, welcoming strangers and telling them their story.

One day, as Philemon was standing on the steps relating the history of the temple, Baucis saw that a strange thing was happening. Philemon was growing leaves! She cried out in surprise, and Philemon turned to look at her. He saw that she too was growing leaves, and was changing into a tree.

"Farewell, dear wife," he said, and immediately a leafy crown grew above his hoary head, and he was a mighty oak. Baucis, too, was changed into the same kind of tree, and with their leaves they touched each other and whispered softly in the wind.

And still, so it is said, the shepherds show the trees to travelers, telling the strange tale of how they came to be there, so close together.

The Statue that Came to Life

Pygmalion, the King of Cyprus, was a sculptor. His clever fingers carved images of the gods and goddesses, and so beautiful were they that all men marveled at them.

The sculptor would not marry. He did not like women, and vowed that he would never fall in love. Year after year went by, and still there was no queen to share his throne.

One day Pygmalion resolved to make the statue of a woman. Always he had carved and chiseled the likenesses of gods and goddesses, but now he wished to try his skill on the statue of an ordinary woman.

He set to work. Day after day he patiently wrought at a great piece of ivory, striving to bring the form of a beautiful woman from it. Soon the ivory took shape beneath his skillful fingers, and a wonderful statue stood in his workshop.

When it was finished, the sculptor looked long at it. He thought it beautiful – far more beautiful than the gods and goddesses he had wrought before. The face was very lovely, with the dawn of a smile on it. One hand was outstretched as if to take his, and the sculptor took it, and caressed it.

"Oh, lovely statue!" he said, "if you were alive I would love you, and make you my queen. Never have I seen a maiden like you before! You are beautiful beyond

compare."

Every day the sculptor came to gaze upon his beloved statue. He called her Galatea, dressed her in fine garments, and crowned her with flowers. He placed a bracelet upon her outstretched wrist, and hung jewels round her slender neck. He was in love with his statue, but, alas! she could not love him in return.

Soon there came the feast of Venus, the goddess of love. Pygmalion went to her temple, and offered up a prayer.

"Great Queen of Love, hear me!" he said. "Grant that my beautiful statue may smile upon me! Grant that she may love me as I love her!"

Venus listened to his strange prayer. She heard what he said, and on her altar she sent up three tongues of flame. Pygmalion saw them, and felt his heart leap like the flames. Surely Venus would answer his prayer?

He went swiftly back to his workshop. There stood Galatea, his lovely statue, her hand outstretched as always. She was no woman, she was ivory, hard and cold. Pygmalion was bitterly disappointed. He had expected to find his statue alive, ready to welcome him lovingly.

He took the outstretched hand, and stroked it longingly. He looked into the beautiful face with its dawning smile – then his heart began to beat quickly, loudly – for surely the eyes were looking at him, surely the eyelids quivered, and the cheeks flushed red?

Then Pygmalion knew that his great wish was granted. His statue was coming to life! The eyes shone blue, the lips became crimson, and a shy smile spread over the lovely face. The hand he held became soft and warm, and trembled within his.

"Galatea! Galatea! Can you speak? Can you move?" asked the happy king. "Say but one word to me, I beseech you!"

"Pygmalion, my love!" said the living statue, and gave him her other hand. She stepped down from her pedestal beside the king, and he marveled to see his statue walk with such grace. But she was no longer a statue; she was

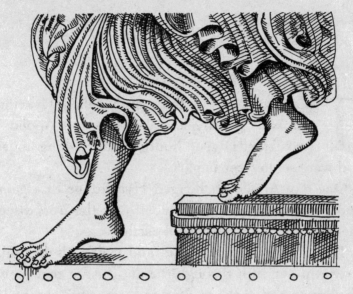

warm and living, soft and sweet.

In delight the king told her of his great love for her, while Galatea listened happily. And soon the two were wedded, and the lovely woman sat by his side, no longer a beautiful image of ivory, but a sweet and loving queen.

The Story of Hyacinthus

There was once a fair youth called Hyacinthus, who was greatly loved by the god Apollo. The two friends went hunting and fishing together, and were seldom seen apart.

One day Apollo challenged Hyacinthus to a game of quoits, vowing that he would throw the iron discus at the mark, and would strike it easily.

The god took the quoit, and, with all his mighty strength, hurled it through the air. Just at that moment, Zephyrus, god of the south wind, came by. He too loved Hyacinthus, and was jealous because the youth liked Apollo best.

Seeing that Apollo hoped to hit the mark with his far-flung discus, the wind-god spitefully blew it aside. But, alas! when it fell to earth it struck the watching Hyacinthus, and smote him a fearful blow on the head.

The youth fell to the ground, fatally wounded. Apollo ran to him in dismay, and took him into his arms. He tried to stanch the wound, but in vain. In a few moments the boy was dead.

"Oh, Hyacinthus, I have robbed you of your life!" said Apollo, in sorrow. "Never will I forget you, but in song and story I will tell your name, and your life-blood shall

spring to beauty as a flower."

As the god spoke, the youth's blood dried up on the ground, and from it sprang beautiful flowers, which bore his name, hyacinth.

The god of the south wind, grieved to see that he had caused the death of the youth he loved, watched tenderly over the spot where the flowers grew, caressing them, and whispering to them endlessly.

And every springtime, when hyacinths blossom in the woods, the south wind visits them, murmuring to the listening flowers his sorrow for the jealousy of long ago.

The Story of Cupid and Psyche

There was once a king who had three daughters. The two eldest were very beautiful, but the youngest, Psyche, was so lovely that men could find no words to describe her. People came from far and near to see her, and whenever she walked abroad, flowers were thrown in her path for her little feet to tread upon.

"She must be Venus herself, the goddess of beauty and love!" cried those who watched her. "We will call her Venus, and we will worship her as a goddess!"

Now when Venus heard this, she was very angry.

"What!" she cried. "Is there a mortal girl who dares to think that her beauty compares with mine! I will punish her!"

She called her son Cupid to her, and he came, carrying with him his arrows of love.

"My son," she said, "there is a mortal maiden whom people worship for her beauty. Go to her tonight and slay her. Then those who worship her will know that she is mortal, and will be afraid."

Cupid filled a vase with some deadly poison and went to find Psyche. She lay asleep in her father's palace, her arm flung around her head. Cupid went to her, and was

about to poison her when the moon suddenly shone out
from behind a cloud, and lit up the maiden's face.

·Cupid stepped back in surprise, for never had he seen
such a lovely maiden before. He dropped one of his own
arrows upon his foot, and at once his heart became full

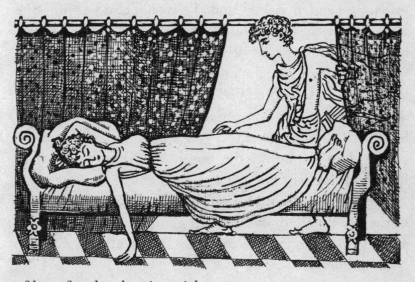

of love for the sleeping girl.

He leaned over Psyche, and drank in her wonderful
beauty. He vowed that he would never hurt her, and
when day dawned, he stole away as quietly as he had
come.

In the morning Venus looked down to the palace to
see if Psyche was dead. To her astonishment she saw her
running in the gardens, playing happily with the pigeons

there. Venus flew into a rage, and resolved to plague the poor girl and torment her in so many ways that she would no longer wish to live.

Day after day things happened to make Psyche miserable. There seemed no end to them, and at last the unhappy maiden vowed that she would end her life. She would climb up to the top of a high mountain, and throw herself down into the valley below.

She climbed wearily up to the top, and then threw herself over. But Cupid was watching her lovingly, angry with his mother for tormenting the maiden so mercilessly. As soon as he saw Psyche cast herself down, he called upon Zephyrus, the South Wind, to catch her in his arms, and bear her away to a distant isle.

Then Psyche found herself caught up in the soft arms of the South Wind, and carried gently through the air to a far-away island. Here she was laid gently down on a bank of flowers.

She arose, and looked round her wonderingly. She found herself in a beautiful garden, where thousands of fragrant roses blossomed. Near at hand was a lovely palace. She walked towards it, and as she came near, the doors swung open to receive her.

Then gentle, unseen hands came about her, and soft voices spoke in her ear.

"Welcome, lovely maiden!" said the voices. "Enter and behold what is yours! Would you eat? You shall find all you need, and all that you love best. Would you sleep? You shall find a bed of down awaiting you, and sweet music to play you to sleep."

Psyche was amazed and delighted. She entered the beautiful palace, and found a marvelous feast set ready for her. Then she found a pretty bedroom, with a bed of down, as the voices had said.

That night, when it was dark and his face could not be seen, Cupid came to Psyche.

"Do not be frightened, beautiful maiden," he begged her. "I love you, and I want you to be my wife. But you must not see my face, nor seek to find out who I am, for then our happiness would depart."

At first Psyche was frightened, but she soon lost her fear, for Cupid was so gentle and loving that she could not help but love him in return. All night long he stayed with her, and when he left she wept.

"I will return tonight," he promised. "Do not weep,

pretty Psyche. I love you, and you are safe here in my beautiful palace. Everything you want you shall have, for I will grant all you wish."

Psyche smiled happily. Then she fell asleep till the golden sunshine flooded her room, and made it light. All day she ran in the garden, playing with the flowers and birds, longing for night to come when Cupid would return.

Each night the god of love came to his gentle wife and made her happy with his soft voice and many gifts. But never did she see his face, nor did she know who he was. She did not even wonder who he could be, for she was quite happy when she was with him – but soon she found the days so long without him that she sighed for company.

"Bring my sisters here to visit me," she begged Cupid. "I am lonely when you are not with me, and I would like to speak with them again."

"They will only bring you unhappiness," said Cupid. "Forget them, Psyche, and be happy by yourself."

But Psyche would not be happy until Cupid had promised to bring her sisters to her. So one morning the South Wind was sent to fetch them, and Psyche found them wandering in the palace gardens, amazed to find themselves so suddenly brought from their home.

How pleased the lonely girl was to see them! She ran to them and kissed them, asking them a hundred questions. She led them to the palace and showed them all the marvels of it. She bade them seat themselves at the table, and then commanded her invisible servants to bring forth a wonderful feast.

While they were eating, the two sisters asked Psyche how she had come to such a beautiful palace, and who had given it to her. They were astonished and jealous, for their own homes were poor and mean compared with their little sister's.

"My husband gave me this palace and all that is in it," said Psyche. "He grants my every wish, and is full of love for me."

"What is he like?" asked the sisters.

Psyche wondered what to say. She did not know what her husband looked like, for she had never seen him.

"He is kind and loving," she said at last.

"But what is his face like?" asked the sisters. "Is he young or old, handsome or ugly? And where is he? Why does he not come to greet us?"

Poor Psyche! She did not know what to answer. Her sisters saw that she blushed and looked down, and they knew that there must be something strange about their sister's husband.

They asked her so many questions about him, that at last Psyche confessed that she did not know what her husband was like, for she had never seen him.

"He comes when it is dark, and will not let me see his

face," she said. "But I do not mind, for he is so kind and loving that I have no wish to know who he is."

"He is a monster!" cried one of the sisters. "Be sure he is an ugly monster, Psyche! Else why should he not let you see him, or know his name?"

"These monsters pretend to love you, and then one night they devour you!" said the other sister cruelly.

"Oh no, no, no!" wept Psyche, frightened and dismayed.

"You must be careful," said her sisters. "See, we will tell you what to do. Tonight, get ready a lamp and a knife. When your husband is asleep, light the lamp and gaze on him. If he is indeed a monster, slay him with your knife!"

"I will do as you bid me," said Psyche. "But now go, sisters. You have made me unhappy, and I would be alone."

The South Wind caught up the jealous sisters, and bore them back to their homes, leaving poor Psyche weeping bitterly.

"He must be a monster!" she thought. "Why should he not show me his face, or tell me his name, if he is not a monster? I must make ready the lamp and the knife."

She hid a lamp behind a curtain, and put a knife beside it. Then she waited tremblingly for her husband to come.

As soon as it was dark, Cupid came. He embraced

Psyche lovingly, and kissed her soft hair. but she would not caress him in return, for she feared him to be a monster, as her sisters had said. Cupid was grieved to find her so silent, but soon he fell asleep, for he was very tired.

As soon as she heard him breathing regularly, and knew him to be sleeping, the frightened girl lighted her lamp, and took up her knife. She held the light over Cupid's face, and looked down on him, expecting to see some fearful monster, ugly beyond belief.

But what did she see? In amazement and delight Psyche gazed on her husband. Lying on the couch was a handsome youth, his head covered with golden curls, and from his shoulders sprang two snow-white wings. Psyche was so surprised that her hand trembled, and the lamp tilted.

A drop of burning oil fell on to the sleeping god's shoulder, and he awoke in pain. He gazed up at Psyche in astonishment and grief, looking on the knife in wonder.

He leapt from the couch, picked up his bow and arrows, and flew from the window.

"Farewell, farewell!" he cried. "I come no more!"

Psyche began to weep bitterly, reproaching herself for thinking that her loving husband could have been a monster. She wished that she had trusted him—but it was too late. She had lost him.

Suddenly a furious wind began to blow, and the palace rocked to and fro. In terror, Psyche ran into the gardens, and fell down in a faint.

When she opened her eyes again, the sun was high in the sky. The palace had disappeared, and where once the lovely garden had been, was now only a rocky wilderness.

Psyche rose to her feet, and looked around. She did not know where to go nor what to do. At last she began to walk westwards, longing to find her husband, and beg his forgiveness.

On and on she went, weeping and asking all she met if they had seen Cupid. But none could tell her anything of her lost husband. At last she met the goddess Ceres, who, remembering the great grief she had felt when she had lost her daughter Proserpina, was sorry for the weeping girl.

"Cupid is with his mother, the goddess Venus," she told Psyche. "He is ill of a fever, for his shoulder is burnt, and pains him very much."

Then Psyche wept more bitterly than ever, for she knew that it was she who had burnt his shoulder.

"What shall I do?" she asked. "Will Venus ever forgive me?"

"Go and ask her pardon," said Ceres. "She was once jealous of you because you are beautiful, and now she is angry because you have robbed her of her son, and have hurt him sorely."

So Psyche went to ask pardon of Venus. She knelt down before the angry goddess, and begged for forgiveness.

"Make me your servant," she said. "I will serve you well, great goddess."

Venus was very angry. She determined to set Psyche such difficult tasks that she would not be able to do them.

She led her to a great heap of barley, wheat, beans, peas, and millet.

"Sift all these seeds one from another," she said. "Have your task done by the sunset. Only by such labor as this will you earn your husband, foolish girl."

Poor Psyche! She knew that she could not sort out all the different seeds by the evening. She sat down in despair and began to weep and wail.

A little ant heard her cries, and came running up. When he saw what was the matter, he went to fetch his many companions. All day long the little insects toiled for Psyche, carrying the different grains into different piles. When sunset came, the task was done.

Venus was greatly astonished.

"This is not done by *your* hands!" she cried wrathfully. She threw Psyche a crust of bread, and left her alone in the darkness.

Next day she came again, and showed a Psyche a high hill, on the top of which a herd of wild sheep were feeding among the brambles.

"They are as fierce as lions," said the angry goddess. "I want a handful of their fleece. Go, fetch it for me."

Psyche climbed up the steep hill – but when she came near the rams, and saw them butting at one another fiercely, she was afraid. Then she heard a soft voice speaking to her from a nearby pool.

"Maiden, do not go near the rams while the sun is hot, for then they are fierce, and will kill you. Wait until the shadows fall upon the hillside, and then they will lie down in peace. You can then climb up to the brambles, and pluck the fragments of golden fleece they have left hanging here and there on the thorns."

So Psyche waited patiently till the shadows fell upon the hillside where the rams fought. Then they lay down peaceably, and the maiden was able to climb up and pick a handful of golden fleece from the thorns.

Venus was full of anger when she found that Psyche

had been able to perform this task.

"So once again you have had help!" she mocked. "Tomorrow I will give you a task in which no one can help you."

The next day Venus showed Psyche a strong black stream, that fell down a mountainside some way off.

"Take this crystal urn, climb up to the stream's source, and fill it for me, bringing it back before sunset," she commanded.

Psyche set off, carrying the urn. But as she climbed upwards, she saw that fierce dragons guarded the way, and her heart sank within her, for she knew she would be devoured. She fell to the ground in terror, and wondered what to do.

Then a great eagle saw her and swooped downwards.

"Foolish girl!" he screamed. "What are you doing here? Go back before you are devoured. You cannot steal a single drop from the sacred spring, for the way is guarded too well."

Psyche looked at the eagle in despair. The great bird was touched by her sad face, and taking the urn from her hand, he flew upwards, carrying it in his beak.

"I will do your task for you," he said.

Presently he returned with the urn full of ice-cold water from the stream's source. Psyche took it gratefully, and the eagle flew away. Then, very carefully, the girl descended the mountain once more.

But Venus was still enraged with Psyche, and devised yet more difficult tasks, till the poor maiden became pale and worn with so much weary work. All this time Cupid was lying in his mother's palace, ill of his fever. But one day he flew from the window, hearing that the maiden he loved was being tormented once again by his mother.

Soon he found Psyche in a faint by the wayside, and she looked so pale and sad, that the god of love was full of pity and love for her. He kissed her tenderly, and she opened her eyes.

What joy was in her heart when she saw her beloved husband once more, and heard him speak loving words! Cupid bade her have no more fear, and took her with him to Olympus, the mountain of the gods. There he begged Jupiter to let his wife drink the nectar of the gods, which would make her a child of heaven like himself.

Jupiter consented, and Psyche was given a goblet of the wonderful nectar. She drank it and became immortal. Then a great wedding feast was held on Mount

Olympus, and the two were united before all the gods.

Soon Psyche was taken once again to the wonderful palace, and there she lived in happiness with her husband, seeing him not only by night, but by day as well.

The Wings of Icarus

There was once a very clever man called Daedalus. Minos, the King of Crete, bade him make a labyrinth full of passages that turned here and there, crossed one another, and twisted and wound about in such a way that no one could find his way out, once he was in.

Daedalus made a marvelous maze, and the king was delighted with it; but before long a quarrel came between the two, and Minos shut Daedalus up in a tower. With him was his young son, Icarus.

For a long time Daedalus tried to escape, and at last he did so. But Crete was an island, and as soon as the king heard that his prisoner had gone from the tower, he set guards round the coast, with orders to search every ship before it sailed from Crete.

Daedalus knew this, and despaired of escaping from the island. But at last he bethought himself of the air.

"Minos may be king of land and sea," he said, "but he is not ruler of the air! I will escape on wings!"

He gathered together a great heap of soft feathers, and sorted them out into large and small. Then, beginning with the smallest, he stuck them tightly together with wax. When he came to the large ones he threaded them one to the other, and in this way made a marvelous pair of wings.

When they were finished, he fastened them to his shoulders, and casting himself down from a height, was delighted to find that he could fly! He flew here and there, and then satisfied that he really could fly, he floated down to his wondering son, Icarus.

"Make me some wings too," begged Icarus. "I will help you!"

The boy began to sort out the feathers for his father. Daedalus stuck them together with wax, and then threaded the larger ones just as he had done for his own wings. Soon a second pair was ready, and with

trembling fingers Daedalus fastened them to his son's shoulders.

"You must practice first," he told him. "We cannot fly from this island over the sea to the distant land, unless you know how to manage your wings. Even the birds must learn to fly."

Icarus soon learned how to manage his big feathery wings. In delight his father watched him flying here and there, up and down, like a great bird. When he saw that his boy could manage his wings wisely and cunningly, he made plans for their escape.

"We will start when the sun rises," he said, "for we must have all the day to see our way over the sea. Sleep well, Icarus, and rise early."

When the sun rose, Daedalus fastened on his own wings, and then strapped the second pair to his son's shoulders.

"Follow me," he said. "Do not fly too low, or the spray from the sea will damp your wings, and clog the feathers. Do not fly too high, or the sun will melt the wax from your wings, and then you will fall. Fly along the middle way, and you will be safe."

So saying, he rose into the air, followed by the excited youth. High they flew, over the fields and hills, and shepherds and ploughmen cried out in amazement to see such a strange sight.

"See, there fly two gods!" cried the onlookers, and fell upon their knees in awe.

Soon Daedalus and Icarus left the island behind, and flew over the sea. Icarus was excited and happy, and soon, feeling safe on his big wings, he flew higher into

the air. He was cold, and when the sun warmed him, he flew higher still, rejoicing in the heat.

But soon he flew too high, and the sun began to melt the wax that held the feathers together. They became loose and floated down to the sea. Icarus beat his arms up and down in fear – but his wings would no longer bear him. Down he fell, and down, and at last the sea swallowed him, and he was drowned.

Daedalus suddenly turned to see if his son was close behind. When he missed him, he called out in fear.

"Icarus! Icarus, my son, where are you?"

But there was no reply. In despair, Daedalus flew down to the waters, and there, floating lightly on the waves, were the feathers that had been in his son's two wings.

Then Daedalus knew that Icarus was drowned, and he lamented bitterly. He found the body of his son, and carried it to land, grieved that he alone should arrive alive and safe. In memory of Icarus, he called the waters the Icarian Sea, and to this day they bear the same name.

The Boastful Spinner

There was once a fair maiden called Arachne, who was very clever with her loom and her needle. She wove such beautiful pictures that not only did men and women come to watch her, but even the nymphs left their woods and streams to see her quick fingers.

Arachne was vain. She thought that no one in the world could equal her in embroidering marvelous pictures. She loved to see the people standing behind her, wondering at her cleverness.

"Surely the great goddess Minerva must have taught this maiden her art," said the onlookers.

Arachne might well have been pleased to hear this, for the goddess was famous for her skill with the needle; but instead she was angry, and tossed her pretty head proudly.

"Minerva could teach me nothing!" she said. "If she came to me, she would learn many things, for I am better at weaving than she is!"

This proud boast of Arachne's came to the ears of the goddess. She arose and dressed herself as an old woman, meaning to give the foolish maiden some good advice. Soon she stood by Arachne's side, watching the girl weaving a beautiful picture.

It was not long before the maiden began to boast again. She spoke lightly of Minerva and her skill, not knowing that the great goddess herself stood behind her.

"Put a guard upon your tongue, maiden," said Minerva. "Your proud words will come to the ears of the goddess, and she will punish you. Be warned in time, and beg her for forgiveness. She is merciful and will pardon you. Beautiful as your work is, it can easily be bettered by Minerva, and this you surely know yourself."

Arachne was very angry. She turned upon the old crone, and spoke rudely to her.

"Keep your advice until it is wanted," she said. "Tell it to your daughters or handmaids! I need no lessons from you, old woman! I tell you, I know what I am saying – Minerva could not do better work than I, and she knows it! If she thinks otherwise, why does she not come to try her skill with me?"

"She is here before you!" said the old woman. She suddenly threw off her long cloak, and stood upright in all her beauty and majesty.

The men and women, and the nearby nymphs, fell upon their knees and paid her homage. Only Arachne stood upright. She flushed a bright red, and then she paled. She was still defiant, and would not beg for mercy, or ask pardon for her bold words.

"Set up a new loom," commanded Minerva. "You shall

try your skill with me as you wish. Choose a design, and I will do the same. We will set to work with our needles, and at the end the two pictures shall be judged."

Arachne set up her loom, and Minerva did the same. Then the two rivals took their needles and began to work. The goddess chose for her design a picture of the gods, with the great Jupiter in the midst. She put herself in the picture also, arrayed in all her glittering armor. The wondering onlookers saw her quick needle bring forth designs of wicked mortals being punished by the gods, of giants turned into great mountains, and of foolish girls changed into screaming birds.

Arachne worked swiftly. She was still proud and defiant, and meant to show the goddess that she was not afraid of her.

Under her needle appeared pictures of the gods doing wrong and foolish things. The vain maiden hoped that she would bring a blush to the cheek of Minerva, when her rival looked upon her picture.

At last the designs were finished. The two weavers turned to see each other's work. At the first glance Arachne knew that she had been defeated. Minerva's picture was so marvelously wrought that it seemed to live.

The goddess gazed in anger upon Arachne's work. She saw that the girl had learned nothing from her advice, or her contest – she was still vain and defiant. In rage, Minerva snatched up the embroidery and tore it to pieces. Then she turned to the frightened girl.

Before Arachne could run away, the goddess struck

her. In an instant the maiden shriveled up. All her hair fell off, and her eight fingers turned to legs. She was a spider!

The terrified watchers saw her run across the floor and hide herself in a dark corner, ashamed and miserable. There she began to weave a web, for Minerva still left her the power of making beautiful designs.

And from that day to this, Arachne's children have done nothing else. You can find their marvelous webs wherever you look.

Arion and the Dolphin

Arion, the musician, lived at the Court of Periander, King of Corinth. He was a great favorite, for he could make such sweet music with his lyre, and sing such beautiful songs that every one loved and honored him.

One day Arion heard that there was to be a great musical festival in Sicily. He went to King Periander and begged permission to take his lyre overseas with him, and try to win the prizes offered for the sweetest music.

"Do not go, Arion," said Periander. "Stay here with me, for I shall miss you sadly if you go far away. There is no music like yours."

But Arion begged so hard to go that at last Periander agreed. At once the musician set off for the far land of Sicily, taking only his lyre with him.

He easily won all the prizes offered, and was crowned the king of music. Then, laden with gold and jewels, he prepared to return to Corinth, eager to see his friend Periander, and to show him his treasures. He hired a ship to take him home, and prayed for fine weather.

The gods answered his prayer for a calm sea – but the voyage was not a fortunate one for Arion. The sailors on the ship caught sight of all the gold and the jewels that the singer had with him, and at once they began to plan to get it for themselves.

"We will kill him, and take his wealth," they said. "No one will know, for Corinth is far from Sicily. We will say that we have left him happy and famous in that distant land."

They went to Arion, and bade him make ready for death.

"Either we will slay you here, and bury you on shore, or you may cast yourself into the sea," they said.

"If it is my wealth that has turned you into pirates, take it for yourselves," said Arion. "But as for me, let me go, I pray you. Only give me my lyre – that is all the treasure I need."

The wicked sailors laughed.

"You will have to die," they said. "If we take your wealth and set you free, you will tell King Periander what we have done, and we shall be punished. No, no, you must die. Choose quickly whether we shall slay you, or whether you shall cast yourself into the waves."

"I will throw myself into the sea," said Arion. "But, first, grant me a wish. Let me dress myself in my loveliest garments, those which I wore when I was crowned king of music in Sicily, and let me sing one last song. Then I will do as you wish."

The pirates would not have granted such a wish, but Arion was so famous that they longed to hear his music;

so they bade him garb himself as he wished, and sing to them.

The musician dressed himself in flowing robes of gold and purple, scented his long hair, and placed his golden wreath upon his head. In his left hand he held his lyre, and in his right the slender ivory wand with which he swept the strings. He strode to the side of the vessel, and, looking down on the deep blue waves, began his last song.

His voice was so beautiful, his song so lovely, and the sounds from his lyre so sweet that the listening sailors were entranced. Their hearts filled with pity, and they almost repented of their cruelty.

When Arion had finished singing, he cast himself into the sea. The ship held steadily on her way, and soon the sailors forgot the pity they had felt, and joked as they

divided his wealth among them.

Now, so sweet had been the singer's music that a herd of dolphins had been attracted to the ship. They had swum behind it, listening eagerly, enchanted by the delicious sounds that came on the breeze. When Arion threw himself into the water, they saw him, and came swimming round him.

The biggest dolphin of all knew Arion to be the maker of the sounds he had loved. He swam up to him, and offered his broad back to the struggling musician. Gladly Arion climbed upon it, and, holding his precious lyre safely out of the water, marveled at his good fortune.

Swiftly the dolphin swam towards the nearest coast. Hour after hour he swam, while Arion composed a song in honor of his strange steed, singing it as he was borne along through the restless waves. Then at last land came in sight, and the dolphin left his rider at the shore.

Arion saw the towers of Corinth in the distance, and

hastened towards them, singing as he went. He had forgotten his lost wealth, and was happy to think that he would soon see his friend Periander once again.

When he arrived at the court, the king took him in his arms and embraced him, delighted to see his musician back in safety.

"I come to you once more," said Arion. "But alas, Periander, I cannot show you the gold and the jewels that I gained in Sicily, for the pirates in my ship stole it all away. And I should have drowned, if it had not been for a kindly dolphin that brought me to land."

Periander listened in amazement as Arion told him all his story. When he heard of the cruel sailors, he was very angry.

"I will punish them," he cried. "When they come to Corinth, I will command them to appear at court, and I will ask them what has become of you. You shall conceal yourself, and appear to them when the right time comes!"

The next day the ship sailed into the harbor. The king sent word for the sailors to come to his court, and very soon they arrived.

"Have you heard aught of the musician Arion?" asked Periander. "I am anxious for news of him."

"He is in the town of Tarentum, well, prosperous, and happy," answered the sailors untruthfully. "We left him there, lord, and he bade us tell you of his happiness."

At that moment Arion stepped forth from his hiding-place, and faced the amazed sailors. He was dressed in purple and gold, and on his head was a golden wreath. He looked exactly the same as when he had leapt into the sea.

The sailors fell flat on their faces in awe and terror. They felt certain that Arion must be a god, for had they not seen him cast himself into the waters? And who but a god could so marvelously appear before them, in the same garb?

King Periander looked sternly upon the sailors, and they trembled.

"Where is the wealth you took from Arion?" asked the king. "Bring it here, and lay it at his feet. Then prepare yourselves for death. Such a crime as yours can have no other reward."

The sailors returned all the treasures they had stolen. But when the king would have ordered them to be slain, the musician stepped forward.

"Let them live," he said. "I do not want them to die. Banish them to another land, oh king. That will be punishment enough."

So the wicked sailors took ship once more, and set sail for distant lands, glad to have escaped with their lives.